GREAT WORLD CIRCUS

Other books by William Kotzwinkle

ELEPHANT BANGS TRAIN

HERMES 3000

NIGHTBOOK

THE FAN MAN

SWIMMER IN THE SECRET SEA

DR. RAT

FATA MORGANA

HERR NIGHTINGALE AND THE SATIN WOMAN

JACK IN THE BOX

E.T. THE EXTRA-TERRESTRIAL

CHRISTMAS AT FONTAINE'S

GREAT WORLD CIRCUS

WILLIAM KOTZWINKLE

ILLUSTRATED BY

JOE SERVELLO

G. P. PUTNAM'S SONS/NEW YORK

Library of Congress Cataloging in Publication Data

Kotzwinkle, William.
Great world circus.

I. Title.
PS3561.Q85G7   1983   811'.54   82-18537
ISBN 0-399-12784-4

Printed in the United States of America

GREAT WORLD CIRCUS

The High Priestess of Ur cannot enter a tavern
    under penalty of death.
On the hotel stair, the businessman feels short of breath,
and Gustav Claudin, insomniac, walks the empty square,
    while British Plague Inspectors in Singapore
    go through the city, stopping at every door.
These times and figures have converged in oracular water,
    each playing its part with the temple daughter
        as she veils her face
        a veil of lace
        sewn with figures of the zodiac.

Despite the rule, she enters a saloon in Ur.
A baboon grabs her by the wrist, pointing to the ale
  —a soldier tries to lift her veil,
  and she vanishes through a magic aperture
  into worlds far from Ur,

along the sea lanes of the Johore Strait
appearing at a Chinese temple gate
in a teeming slum
noted for its smell of opium.

This is Singapore, gateway of the East.
A Buddhist priest bows to her
then consults his calendar
wondering what has caused this apparition,
a sorceress of such erudition
appearing from another age.
The venerable sage ponders the design
as the priestess continues on past his shrine,
blending into the crowd of Malaysian and Chinese,
and British women at their ease
somewhat fatalistically accepting life in the tropics.
Death has lately been one of the topics—
the plague having taken much of the bloom
that formerly glowed in their drawing room.

Then:
    Bead curtains parted, sunlight streamed through;
    the High Priestess entered from the avenue
    into a tea shop, dark-paneled, cool,
    two porcelain dogs on the vestibule,
    the dogs turning as she walked past,
    their ceramic eyes discerning her origin from enchanted glass,
    or from water?
    No matter, an oracle's daughter,
    made of elements liable to fade.
    The waiter sat her in the shade,
    thinking only that she was English
    and sensitive to the heat.

She thanked him, her eyes on the street,
where the Plague Inspectors walked,
and she looked at one of them, as if she stalked
that starched white-uniformed government man,
    so confident, so cosmopolitan.

Feeling her gaze, he stopped.
In another moment, he'd entered the shop
and seated himself at her table.
"You are new here, if there is anything I am able to do—"
He twisted his mustache, set his white helmet down.
He could not see her invisible crown,
surmounted by a bumblebee,
assumed she was employed by the tea company,
with much to learn and everything to fear.

"Well, I'll tell you what we do for excitement here—"

He described the club, the government grounds,
    could not hear the peculiar sounds
    that came from the porcelain dogs at the door.
"This Singapore—it is bearable, you see,
    once you've got hold of its topography . . ."

He gestured with his slender cane.
"You'll find much about which to complain, and yet—"

How astonishing are her eyes
how smooth her skin.
"Everything here is owned by our mandarin . . ."
He pointed to the street, the balconies.
"You grow used to it, by degrees."
He elaborated, sipped his tea, then suddenly
noticed that the woman's form was fading,
as rainbows do
beautiful colors dissolving into air,
a strange buzzing in her hair,
as if it were filled with bees.

"You'll grow used to it," she whispered, *"by degrees . . ."*
then disappeared
into a screen of bamboo.

The Inspector turned slowly toward the avenue,
and the bright arcade,
his head momentarily made of jade.
"I've been too long in Asia . . ."
He tapped his knee gently with his cane,
wondering how he might see her again.

17

Gustav Claudin of sleepless nights
     walks the thoroughfares,
following the glowing lamppost lights,
     climbing the public stairs—

he feeds the cats who live below,
     their eyes a smaller lamp
as they pace nervously to and fro
     within their hidden camp.

Some are indifferent, feigning sleep
     only to make a sudden leap
upon the morsel of midnight he brings.
"You little sovereigns, you outlawed kings . . ."
He does not stroke them,
but has heard whispered talk
concerning the mystery they stalk.
It is the bird of darkness,
     bearing the song of the moon.
     They hunt it by the public lagoon,
     this tiny cantatrice.

And in their eyes, Claudin is a priest
     of their order,
bearing offerings at the border.
In return, they have given him a clue
     as to what it is he must do
     to end his fast from sleep.

But the tongue of cats is deep,
 symbols beyond men.
Gustav Claudin will have to come again,
 night after night
 with milk and fish
laying them down and repeating his wish.

Now he takes a gold watch from his vest
 —it mocks his endless search—
the last time he slept was in Budapest
 for a moment, in the back of a church.

But perhaps the little magicians of the park
 are preparing him an answer in the dark
  for they have been seen
   dancing
  as a woman's form took shape
  down beside the misty lake.

Claudin walks on,
 with many lampposts yet ahead,
 a boulevard garlanded
 and somehow feminine.
 She is a night-black harlequin,
 diamond patterns on her sleeves;
 with distant laughter she deceives
 her straining lover as he listens.
 He hurries, to where the footpath glistens.

The Scribe of the Temple Records wrote in a steady hand
with his sacred baboon nearby,
tail wrapped round the water-stand.

Let us light our torch and make libation . . .

The baboon chortled, clicked his teeth, attempting communication,
and the Scribe, with a sigh, set aside his pen.
"Have you been into the ale again?"

The baboon nodded and beat his chest.

"You've had all you're getting today," said the Scribe,
   but the baboon repeated his request,
   beating his tail, standing on his head.

"Listen," said the Scribe, "I'm writing odes to the dead,
and you—" He pointed to the door. "—are going *out.*"
   The baboon went into a pout
   and the Scribe continued to write.

   . . . make our libations to the gods who preside over the night . . .

The herbalist turned, hearing a hesitant footfall.
The Plague Inspector had entered the stall.
The herbalist bowed:
    "You wish—a powder for an enemy's defeat?"

"I was seated," said the Inspector,
    "in a tea house. The light was dim."

He told of the woman who'd appeared to him
    and then vanished into air.
"I've been looking for her everywhere."
"Happens all the time," said the herbalist. "She is
Ore of Mercury, the Lady Cinnabar."
He handed the Inspector a stoppered jar
in which a tiny woman slept.
The Inspector's heart leapt,
for it was she, the creature he'd seen,
with red crystal eyes and gown of fiery opaline.

A transaction was made—the Inspector left the arcade,
the jar in his hand glowing red.
He took it home and placed it on the washstand by his bed.
Lady Cinnabar awoke,
covering him with lemons, oranges, and a golden cloak,
but by dawn these gifts were gone,
as was his bride,
leaving only sulfide on his fingertips
and oil of mercury on his lips.

He hurried back to the arcade
but found instead a seller of jade
in the stall where the herbalist had been.
"Here is a fine piece," said the seller. "A dancing djinn—"

"A moment," said the Plague Inspector.
"What has happened to the herbalist?"
"I am afraid," said the dealer in jade,
"he has ceased to exist."

"You mean he's dead?"

"Dead five-hundred years, though occasionally he reappears
   —his ghost haunts the arcade—
now here is a masterwork of jade, wild geese in flight,
   mounted on a piece of meteorite.
   Business has been slow
   and I might sell it at a price so low—"

"Just a day ago," interrupted the Inspector,
"I bought a tiny woman here,
who vanished without a trace."

"In this world," said the seller,
"all can be replaced."
He lifted up a statuette of clay,
resembling the bride in every way.
"From Tibet," he smiled. "Magically endowed."
The Inspector paid, the dealer bowed.

So began the long parade
of purchases made in the enchanted arcade,
each purchase vanishing with the dawn
and the seller of it also gone,
the Inspector returning to the stall
only to find it beyond recall
and a different seller there
with women of ivory, shell, or earthenware,
among whom would be Lady Cinnabar,
embracing him and fading with the morning star.

This Plague Inspector, this government man,
took to wandering in an old sampan
and smoking with the derelicts of Singapore,
those familiar with his enchanted door,
who with him shared other wonders of the stream,
things they too had found in the dream
that we call time,
    bubble of the orient
    illusion sublime.

34

The baboon staggered down the lane,
grunting and grumbling and drunk again.
He waved a bottle in the air,
then rolled around in the sand,
put some flowers in his hair
and attempted once more to stand.

He swayed there, at the city's heart,
a sacred animal doing his part.
Dimly he viewed the milling throng
and babbled a little baboon song,
then shuffled off, hoping to find
a soldier or someone else inclined
to issue a baboon a drink.

He'd not gone far before beginning to sink
    again
        and then to fall.
He found he could not walk at all.

One too many, he reflected,
    gazing at the sky.
It was then the High Priestess came by.

"Sacred Animal, rise and be saved."

Forgive me, signed the ape, but I'm depraved, as you know.
"Upon you," said the priestess, "I shall bestow—"

—a drink?

"No, you wretched monkey, the ability to think."
She took him by the ear, yanked him to his feet.
He called for ginger beer and something to eat,
but she dumped him in the fountain
and held him underwater.

—please, please, o temple daughter—
He signaled with his tail
that he would imbibe no further ale—today.
"Good," said the priestess, "for it is written
you have magic to convey."

At this, the baboon attempted to appear profound,
making a guttural sound
he hoped would pass for a spell,
for it was his impression that all temple personnel
had access to spice wine
with which a baboon could have a very nice time
in the shade of a sycamore. He signed,
pointing to the temple door.

But the priestess took him by the paw
and invoking higher law
sped with him into space.

The baboon covered his face
as they entered a cosmic hole.
She showed him a certain scroll
　　that read
the greatest magic of the moon
is worked by priestess and baboon.
A drink, he groaned, to steady my nerves.
I know a place that serves children, monkeys, and thieves . . .

They shot through dimensions of dark degrees,
　　along ancient baboon paths
　　through the mystic trees,

paths forgotten, of course, by this drunken ape
but all that was needed was his simian shape
for the paths to appear.
"You," said the priestess, "are my charioteer."

In that case, said the ape, we have much to fear.

Immense worlds floated by
whirling, turning
troubling the eye

but some instinct, buried in baboons,
led them through these baffling ruins
and on, to yet higher states
where the priestess gathered those concentrates
that give men wisdom as well as rest.
The baboon repeated his request
that they return,
but she told him she had much to learn
". . . and places to go, far off in time,
where I am expected to call."

The baboon tried to climb,
a familiar tree, a wall,
but it all slipped through his grip and he had to swim
    in substances alien to him
    in which he swore
    to drink no more
    or at least not so much,
    not to the point he'd touched today,
    where space opens up and you float away.

On they traveled, over the sun,
the work of the priestess just begun.

The gods of stone stand near the temple wall.
Two oxen pull a cart on past the gate.
The driver's face—dimly I recall
a time in which our lives were twined by fate.

This Singapore, this dragon of lost dreams—
its jade-green tail wraps round a glowing bowl.
Along the waterfront a lantern gleams.
Inside its glass you'll find your ancient soul.

Upon this wall an English poster, torn:
Great World Circus—Known to All
"You wish? Droppings of a unicorn . . . ?"
The herbalist bows within his wretched stall.

And all desires have their certain door
this night in sprawling Singapore.

And King Khasekhem built himself a temple of eternal remembrance
at Hierakonpolis

". . . of which only a granite doorpost has survived,"
said the professor,
pouring tea for himself and his guest.
He took a tiny baboon-headed figure from his vest.
"This was a button we found in the sand."

an everlasting temple raised above the land
warning to our enemies
sentinel of time
perfect
magnificent
sublime
forever shining, forever one

"My profession is oblivion," he said, and served dry toast,
    burnt on one side,
then showed a photograph of the celebrated doorpost
and beside it his guide, scowling in the sand
as if beside a parking meter whose time had elapsed.

"Everything else had collapsed, so of King Khasekhem himself
    I can't say we even found his bones—
    we had better luck in the stones of an old dye plant
    —an enormous vat with a gigantic basin—
    and inside it an amazing skeleton,
    not an aristocrat of course
    but a nomad and his horse.
    They must have tumbled through;
    it's strange what sand will do
    in hiding obstacles as well as kings.

"There were preservative solutions below,
   as well as traces of indigo.
   These deep-dyed things are what remain,
   the unknown rider's bridle, brightly stained,
   and his skull, a violet blue.
But as for Khasekhem, not a clue. It is often the way," he said,
   extinguishing the lamp and closing up the room.
In the hall, I examined an ancient ostrich plume,
then noticed from beneath the doorway we'd just passed through
   a faint light, glowing violet blue.

"Yes," he said, seeing my glance,
"I suppose one might call it eternal remembrance . . ."

Leonide Leblanc—
I kept her in gloves and perfume.
Now we meet fleetingly in a sea-room,
her image no more than fog in my hand.

"Leonide, do you understand . . . ?"

She smiles, the smile of a lotus land,
  and fades from sight.
In this way, Gustav Claudin spends the night
  on the boulevard.

"Blanche! Blanche d'Antigny—is it you that I see?
  Do you understand this mystery?"

She smiles and grows shadowy.

*C*an this loneliness be transmuted?
She appeared in a hotel lobby,
and the businessman, feeling suddenly uprooted
followed her past the white piano and the desk,
saw her name on the register,
    a sort of arabesque,
      her key a glyph of the inner planet
      surmounted by a bumblebee.

Led by her perfume
he entered the hotel dining room,
then found he was unable to speak, unable to order,
could only sign with his hand that he wanted water
and the veiled woman did not glance his way.

He continued to stare at her,
into the hidden radiance of Ur.
He thought: *I ought to send over my card with a note.*
But he felt something so remote,
such deep distance behind her veil,
that he lost the scale by which we judge our place in time,
and for an instant, knew the sublime
but thought it was something he'd eaten,
or the disorientation of travel,
not realizing that one can occasionally unravel
the threads of circumstance,
the cloth of our dimension.
Or perhaps it's merely tension, he said to himself
    to steady his grip,
not realizing that one can slip into other worlds
    if the moment unfurls
    some of what it contains,
    at the intersecting of planes
    to Ur and beyond.

Can this loneliness be transmuted?
In the banquet room, occult leaders are meeting
with horoscopes and alphabetical seating.
The businessman passes their open door,
  feeling like a dinosaur,
  lumbering and slow.
The woman is in the hall, and lifts her veil.
An occult leader faints from the glow
but the businessman gives her his calling card.
It turns to flame, he vanishes with her,
and his baggage remains unclaimed.

The occult leaders rest
having agreed on a whole new style.
In Ur, meanwhile, an innkeeper receives a strange guest
  who speaks of things to come
  in far-off lands of the millennium,
  yet claims to be just a businessman
  wandering through Ur, with a caravan.

Miller moths flutter, tossed by the wind,
white wings of white dust, there is no end.
Miller moths flutter, flying in pairs
delighting in love while time is still theirs.

Fish feed on white wings, caught in the stream
swallowing hungrily the miller moth dream.
Miller moths flutter, dancing in pairs,
delighting in love, while time is still theirs.

A brown-headed blackbird with ravenous beak
dines on the white bug who lives for a week.
Miller moths flutter, floating in pairs,
delighting in love, while time is still theirs.

Dead on the window, killed by the heat,
limp in a dewdrop, white wings effete,
miller moths flutter, flying in pairs
delighting in love, while time is still theirs.

How futile the dancing, and hopeless the scheme
of miller moths fluttering in a dream.
Still they go dancing, flying in pairs
delighting in love, while time is still theirs.

There was no furniture in the room, except for the cot on which Monsieur de Beauvoir lay dying.

"I have drunk 150,000 francs worth of champagne," he said with a faint smile, and rolled over, covering his own head.

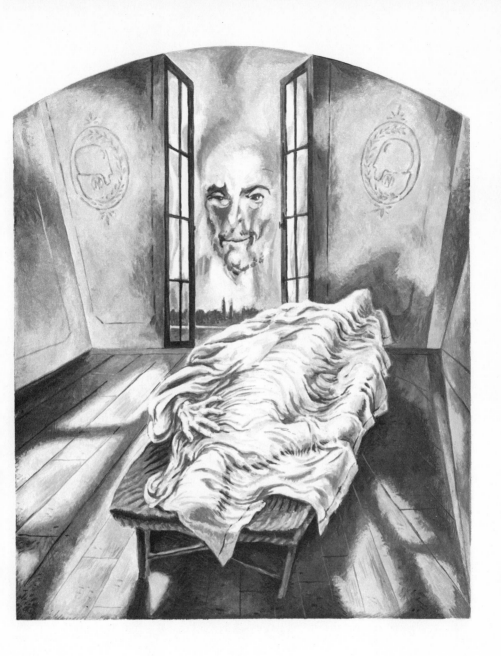

Just below Pigalle, he flies to the spires.
He is but one of numerous fliers.

In the salon of a west coast schooner
   the High Priestess appeared to the second mate.
"I would have come sooner," she said,
   "but I hesitate—"

· "No, no," he said, "sit down, I'm familiar with spirits."
   An imp of the sea was by his shoulder.
"I become more familiar as I grow older," he continued, asking,
   "Where are you from?"

"From Ur, a city vanished."

"I've seen ghosts," he said, "who were famished."
"My needs," she answered, "are filled by the fog, at dawn,
   near seaports, and in men's minds."

"Yes, well," he said, "I've known all kinds."

"Then it is possible," she said, "that you might know—"
"Who?"
"A man from Dilmun, of the sunrise."

"I've known thousands of men, and heard their stories
   as the day dies."

She carried a feather
and touched his door
"You shall know fair weather
in Singapore."

When they docked the Plague Inspector was there,
  and walked with them up the landing stair
    into the city.

"It's good to see an English face—
I know a restaurant or two."
The second mate caught a trace,
  behind bamboo
  of ghostly eyes.
So, he thought, *she is here . . .*

"See someone you recognize?"
  The Inspector tapped his cane.
"They are very likely to disappear. . .
  Our noodle shop is down this lane."

They dined, and the second mate kept glancing into the lamp.

"Some maintain it is the damp—" The Inspector's voice
    was a thin thread. "Others say the drains . . ."

The lamp's interior was inhabited by a creature of flames,
fingertips on fire, light in her hair.
A mandarin passed in his sedan chair,
and a water clock in the corner of the room
    dripped slowly
    with sparkling drops.

"You'll find a number of interesting shops,
and of course you'll visit the Tomb."

The captain and his mates enjoyed their meal,
    a fan turning above the table.
"I get away," said the Inspector, "when I'm able,
    but the place is in my blood, I suppose."

Within the lamp, a rose edged in flame
fell from the woman's hand.

"Yes, I think you'll enjoy our magic land . . ."
    The Inspector called for the bill.
    "Indeed, I'm sure you will."

They walked together into the street.
The second mate heard a voice, discreet,
    hidden in the shadows of a wall.
    He turned, but saw only
    an ancient herbalist in his stall,
    holding dried flowers up to a clouded sun.

"Be careful of that one," said the Inspector.

All the kings of the entire world
from the Upper to the Lower Sea,
those who are seated in throne rooms,
and those who live in other buildings
as well as all the kings of the West land
living in tents brought their heavy tribute
and kissed my feet in Babylon

They brushed the dust from the doorpost.
   Age-old figures came alive.
". . . something about fighting on the seacoast
   and how the King will survive."

They knelt in the sun of the burning land,
   while in the doorpost
   a tiny soldier kept stand.
". . . forty-seven thousand captives taken
by the forces triumphant, never forsaken
   who put the north in fetters . . ."

From the hewn letters a spirit came forth,
turned once, toward the north,
then sank back into the stone.

". . . and the exalted tiara, ours alone,
   descended from the skies . . ."

He wiped the sweat from his eyes.
". . . now the figure of the Queen,
and this, I think, means golden fanfares."
Gently he brushed at the base of the pillar.

      . . . and miller moths flutter, dancing in pairs,
      delighting in love while time is still theirs.

"The famous Spanish tenor on a Victor disc . . ."
Our Sunday afternoon host
reads from the obelisk
while his guest, the famous ghost
toast of the Met, 1923
waits on the turntable in eternity.

The disc begins, with warp and static;
it has lain for years in the attic,
   its ring of dreams asleep.
There are dreams that you can keep
but time will bend them out of shape.
Neither host nor famous tenor can escape.

From the disc come birds of paradise
with wings of fire and song of sacrifice.
   ". . . a voice unique in its power,"
   our host has said.

But I see only images of the dead

—the tenor dining with a young soprano—
there are candles on the table and on the piano,
   and roses and telegrams
   papers and programs
all half-faded, just beyond the flame.
He whispers he is glad she came
   and then I see
other jeweled women in the night
dining with him by candlelight,
   staring seductively.

"... not only for the way it was trained,
but for the emotion it expressed ..."

I watch as if possessed,
the scene shifting as the needle skips—
there are cabs, hotels, steamships,
a house in England, a villa in Rome
and in the background the ticking of a metronome
  as the images pass
like dreams in a looking glass.
I see wind chimes above and a music stand below,
  memories floating in slow adagio
    a terrace, a balcony, a yard,
    the ivory whiteness of a calling card

    walks in the mountains,
    struggle and score,
    premiere performance for an emperor

days float up as the old disc spins
  with operatic heroines
  thundering out of the static
  brilliantly robed, deeply dramatic
  but fading into the light
  fading already on opening night ...

Four actresses, a quiet afternoon—
their dresses trail upon the hardwood floor.
An old piano dreams of some lost tune,
a fern is situated by the door.

The actresses await the matinee,
no doubt a turning point in their careers.
Gustav Claudin will attend today,
one of many chanticleers.

Affair of Honor, foils, mystery,
a gown and a rattan chair.
Red curtains and a lamp complete the scenery.
Claudin's footstep sounds upon the stair.

"Here he is, the one who cannot sleep," she said.
Yes, he thought, I am the walking dead.

*C*aesar appears:
    "I have been your commander for nine years.
    I ask you to defend my reputation . . ."
    (He lights a torch and makes libation)
    "Stand with me—against the assaults of my enemy."

The men of the 13th Legion, loyal, raise their hand.
(The baboon wrapped his tail round the water-stand)
And the wrongs done to Caesar float in Caesar's brain.
He subdues Tunisia and Spain,
    turns around and begins again.

"Only consider," said the Perpetual Dictator,
"with a small expenditure of effort
you can put an end to grave dissension . . ."

The disc turns in another dimension,
the needle makes the old song ascend,
over and over through the quiet air,

and Caesar's head turns on a jardiniere
   trying to catch the curator's eye,
   but the museum class walks on by.

   ". . . my reputation . . . my enemies . . ."

Glaciers shaped the Pyrenees,
shaped the pass where a vagabond lies,
watching the flight of butterflies,
shaped the passageway for Caesar, Hannibal, the Moors.
"Yes," said the tramp, "Caesar's ghost endures."

The tramp was entertaining the priestess and her ape.
   "There is Caesar's spectral shape."
He pointed with a stick to the Valley d'Aure,
where ghostly legions follow their emperor.

"We have pacified the whole of Germany," said Caesar,
"and of Gaul . . ."
The museum class walked down the hall.

"**I** have thoughts," said the tenor, "I cannot express—
nevertheless, dinner? In my chalet?"
She wears some sort of negligee,
   or so he thinks,
not knowing she is a sphinx.
"My place is far above the crowds."
He points to a dreamhouse in the clouds.

"How high you fly," said the priestess.
"Well," said the tenor, "you see, I'm dead."
Then, hearing a noise, he turned his head.
   The baboon was close behind
   on the celestial avenue.

"I was hoping," said the tenor to the priestess,
   "it'd be just me and you."

The priestess was not inclined to part from her pet,
    who followed, smoking a cigarette,
    into the tenor's mental lair.
    The tenor put flowers around in the air
    causing them to appear from his fingers.
        "The scent will linger,
        but the blossoms fade . . ."

    So he began his serenade
but the priestess vanished as they came with the wine,
and the tenor was left staring out his window into time.
    "Such," he reflected, "is the lot of a ghost."
        Toast of the Met, 1923
        High Priestess of Ur, Eternity

King Semersket smote the Beduins of Sinai
the deed engraved in gold
". . . and while I can't substantiate the date,"
said the professor as he turned the ancient plate,
"I venture to guess 3000 years old."

The stone lamp in the study burned
with a flickering flame.
Pursuing the Beduin I came, into the land of fire

"The king wears the high white crown, as you can see.
The Beduin's face is featureless in the rock
and his knee is down . . ."
Watching is the king's bird, the hawk

. . . down, down, down

The lamp flickers, casting shadows on the floor
of a bird, a Beduin, and a king
wandering an endless corridor
searching, searching

The professor to himself:

Overwhelmed again by the stars
I felt the camel drivers
and the sailors
and all men of old who looked at this dome.

Though they have perished now,
while these same constellations turn,
they are of the stars, without a flicker of doubt—
      they return
they won't go out until the stars go out,
                  and even then, they will roam.

Around the cottage, butterflies flit
and music pervades the scene,
for here lives a harpsichord maker named Schmidt
who made the first guillotine.

He was helped with it
by Doctor Antoine Louis,
designer of surgical cutlery
and by Doctor Guillotin himself,
a man concerned with public health.

Guillotin to the French Assembly:
". . . gentlemen, as an act of humanity,
we should have swift, painless decapitation by machine."

A prisoner named Pellitier
is chosen for unveiling day.
"I'm to sneeze into the bran,"
he remarks to the clergyman
accompanying him to the basket filled with feed
into which his head will speed.

"If you have any last words,
you must say them now."

"Father, I know not how."

The Little Chopper glistens.
Nine months later the King himself listens
　　to it gliding down.
One swift painless cut removes his crown
and Doctor Guillotin is next in line,
　　reputation in decline,
but his sentence is transmuted;
　　someone else is executed.

He dies in bed, still in possession of his head,
　　but filled so they say with shame
　　over the painless machine bearing his name.

Doctor Louis shunned fame too,
denying he'd had anything much to do with it.
"Schmidt's machine, I'm afraid. I only advised
　　on the shape of the blade."

And men of gentle nature have been stirred
to fire their revolvers up a chimney

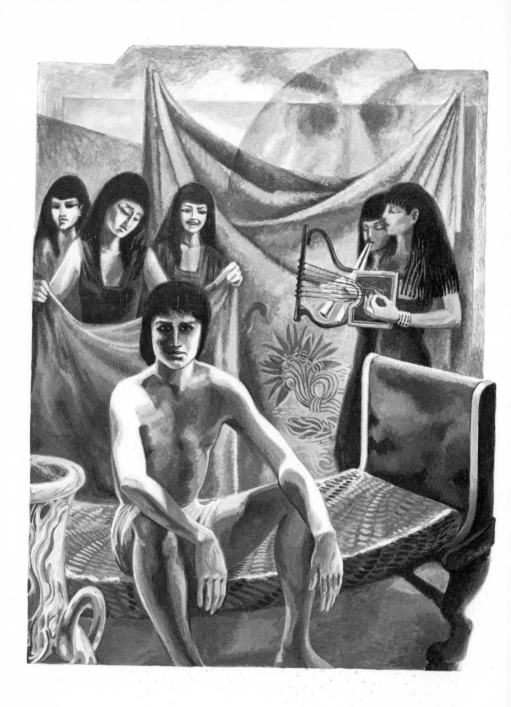

King Zer was wakened every morning
by a maiden's song.
"Hail, O Perfect One,
none can do thee wrong."

The virgins ran his bath
and carried him from his bed,
singing, "None can bear thy wrath,
all must bow their head."

Five-hundred years later,
a thief pulled Zer's dried arm from its socket
and put the King's golden bracelets in his pocket.

He laughed, waving the royal arm.
"My blessings on all of you,
may you escape from harm."

His colleagues ignored the boon,
intent on their own pillage
of the Chamber of the Moon.

"Blessings and prosperity," said the thief,
laughing once more.
He tore the rings from Zer's fingers
and threw the King's arm on the floor.

And the thousand gods of Egypt pursued him

This photograph, of a middle-aged woman in white
   was purchased at an auction sale.
It came inside a trunk with old flowers,
   loose buttons, assorted mail,
a life in miniature, like a shrunken head
   taken by time, her enemy
   and hung in the land of the dead.

The professor and his team found Queen Zer's arm
    over here
    jammed between the stones.

"Bring the lantern, bring it near—how fragile are her bones . . ."

  Withered, my fingers reach out to you, Professor,
      gesturing in the gloom.
      I am yours, with my retinue—
      do not tremble, o my groom

      for I am history, the perfect wife,
      knowledgeable, subtle, complete.
      From the ruins of your mind I waken
      to walk you down an ancient street.

      Hold my fragile body, carry me away.
      I come from the land of the sunrise
          with mouth of fired clay.

      My teachings are silent, neither wind nor reed.
      Contemplate my nature, and examine your greed.

Again the professor reflects:

This feeling, as if some tender thing is gone
and yes, there is much that was and it has gone,
all the men of Zer's day, all of them bone
and the ladies for whom they sighed are flown.
We are alone in our own day, with the stove hot
and the leaves falling, and all that was is not
and this feeling, as if something of mine is gone—
all time is gone, all dreams dreamt,
lost beyond clouds of endless raiment.

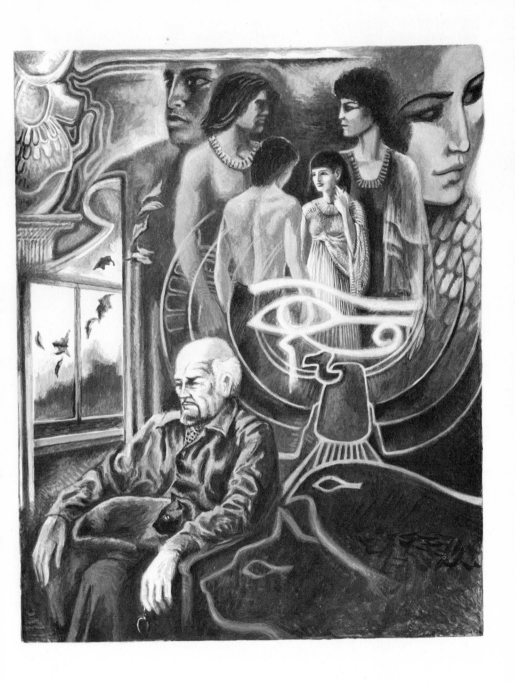

The moment stopped on Sackville Street, northwest,
bright day in spring, 1903,
a gentleman unbuttoning his vest
while in the background a calliope

cranks out a sad forget-me-not
accompanied by the beat of horse's hooves.
The mailman bends to his appointed slot
and all the figures move in timeless grooves

as trolley number 154 bends
slowly round toward O'Connell Bridge
upon a daily trip that never ends
beside a dog on similar pilgrimage.

This memory has shown the ghost all things,
revealing countless secrets, endless springs.

There was something hidden, it's hidden still. Now we chase it, down the hill.

Two girls sit, in eyelet slips, before a Chinese screen.
A crane, white-necked, is walking in the painted scene.
   The photographer goes beneath his hood.
     "Good, hold it please."
   The fire flashes, the camera clicks,
     a day in 1896,
     and time moving by degrees.

The models shift to another pose.
To one of them, the photographer gives a rose.
"Wear it," he says with a smile
and she wonders, all the while,
   what will become of me,
   where shall I wander, whom shall I meet,
   will it be upon the street?

"Very good, ladies, and just turn that rose . . ."
The fire flashes, the camera clicks,
a day in 1896
a photograph called
Beauty in Repose
found in the attic, under moth-eaten clothes.

And where did she wander, whom did she meet?
The answer is bittersweet.
All of it has faded, her dream and the rose,
only the photograph remaining
of Beauty in Repose . . .

123

... though perhaps somewhere
there is a Chinese screen, in disrepair
   with a crane walking in the scene
   like one walking in a dream.

This comical bird, his legs like sticks
   remembers a day in 1896,
remembers the girl with the pale young face
   who vanished into endless space.

And where did she wander, whom did she meet?
   She was loved by a painted bird
   whose love was bittersweet.

Gustav Claudin, beyond ever sleeping again,
   staggers along the thoroughfare,
   eyes tortured by the glare.
His slight form, impeccably attired, is known to the neighborhood.
   It is understood he does not sleep,
   that shopkeepers set their clocks
   to the sound of his cane
   lightly tapping in the lane
and prostitutes feel he is their own
this one who wanders the cobblestone,
shading his eyes from the light,
this spectral knower of the night,
   weary as they are weary
   of all that it holds.

But dawn enfolds them, gives them rest.
Claudin merely opens his vest, at a café,
staring into the wet street
at beginning of day.

Lamps are extinguished on the river,
carriages deliver the morning coal,
and Claudin would happily sell his soul
    could he find a buyer.
He draws his chair near the fire.
The café dog joins him, beneath the table.
"You, my friend," says Claudin softly, "are able
    to do what I cannot.
    What is the formula I have forgot?"

The dog is soon asleep
dreaming of a woman's shape.
He follows, mouth agape,
across a desert land,
but does not understand.
He wakes and rests his chin upon the shoe
of the insomniac of the avenue,
and Claudin feeds him a bit of bun
as together they watch the spreading sun.

I heard the crying somewhere near the dawn
a dying cry of one near gone.
I rose and looked across the yard.
A prince was there, the elegant Renard,
who pounces with delicate feet,
a hunter both dainty and discreet,
and the screams of his victim so near
sounding so loud in my ear
it seemed my own soul must be the feast
for the sun rising in the east.
Then all was still, and yet more still.
Renard on velvet paws went down the hill.

"The inscription," he said, "is something about the kill. Well,
    in any case, the implement is—
a bound Syrian Captive on the Head of a Ceremonial Cane."

I filed it with other artifacts of the buried suzerain,
then suggested that we break, for the light was dim
    and my eyes had begun to ache.
"Yes," he said, "I too am tired, and just now,
    as I lifted this cane,
I thought I heard from the prisoner's lips, a cry of pain."
    He turned to me wearily, and said,
"Can we know who was right or wrong? We are in
    the house of the dead. Either side
    might have been misled. Their causes are dust,
    their rule a dream. Yes, I thought I heard a scream.
    Whose was the victory? Whose the defeat?
                        (*a hunter both dainty and discreet*
                        who pounces with delicate feet)
    "It is emptiness now. Well, let us go and eat . . ."
We stepped out from the chamber subterrane.
"I feel bound by ancient cords," he said,
    "upon an ancient cane."

And I, I felt the same, as if some monstrous vanity
    were humanity's name
    binding us from the beginning
    and binding us still.

                    Renard on velvet paws went down the hill

131

In the hall of the casino, a lone gambler stands,
   cards imprinted on his hands,
   jack, king, and queen.
A woman comes his way, her gown a fiery opaline.

   She wears an evening cloak,
   a diamond pin in her hair.
"I know you," he smiles, "but from where?"

"I come from Ur," she said, "have you been there?"

Together they walked the hall—
from another room came the croupier's call,
while outside a fountain bubbled on the casino grounds.
"There is a game in Ur," she said, "called Jackals and Hounds."

"Never played it," he said, "how does it go?"
Out of the fountain came a faint white glow,
   as flags appeared, with a jackal's head,
   carved in ivory, by the dead.

The jackal flags surrounded the casino grounds.
   "And now," she said, "the hounds."
   Knuckle-bone dogs came from the moon,
   odd-shaped, rough-hewn.

"The board," she said, "is time,
where hounds and jackals have their race."
The gambler looked into her face
and saw his ancient trail,
a succession of squares
through which he'd passed,
with flags of jackals ivory pale
and hounds of bone following fast.

Deep as the board went into antiquity,
it also ran forward to infinity.
    The jackal flags waved,
    the bone-hounds bayed
    and the gambler turned to her.
    But gone was the woman of Ur.

The fountain played in the moonlight,
    music came from the bar.
    He watched a passing satellite
    or was it a wandering star?

He felt a kiss, light as the fountain's spray,
    as he walked across the garden,
    to the call of the croupier.

    He broke the bank by morning,
    an enchanted crowd around.
Odd, thought the weary croupier, *all night I've heard a hound.*

He mentioned it to the owner
at a meeting of the staff.
"Yes," said the owner, "and I a jackal's laugh."

The coin he paid me with had an army on one side
and a banquet on the other.
"I must rise and go to that land," I said.
It is Sumeria, he said.
The land of the dead.

I must rise and go there.

"**M**y name is Pyramidion,"
boasted the King to the High Priestess.
"My beauty shall never fade."

A bed was made for them to lie on
and a servant drew the shade.
The High Priestess removed her gown
and the King his golden crown
while in the courtyard slates were carved
    and monuments erected.
"All these lands," he sighed, "by me are protected."

The peacock feathers spread,
screening off the royal bed.
The sceptre, sheathed in rubies, glowed,
and the King ecstatically bestowed a string of pearls,
placing them in the Ur woman's hand.
"Mysterious creature," he whispered,
    "I know you understand."

Curtains at the window blew gently in,
bringing the scent of jessamine,
and the King scattered diamonds in her hair,
sighing again, but not with despair.

139

Shadows moved upon the wall,
sentries shifted in their stalls
and incensers swayed upon the wind
bringing again the jessamine.

The King drew a feather, traced her breast.
  "Now, my Royal Palimpsest,
erased are all lovers you might have known
  save Pyramidion
  of Egypt's throne."

She smiled and lifted his shining string
  on her fingertips.
  "A weeping spring," she said,
holding the pearls to her lips
where they melted away
like moonlight in the day.

The night of time wore on
—Pyramidion grew old
dying in spring, as foretold.
Centuries later, a piece of his skin graced a slide.
The professor turned to his guide.
"It is soft and flexible. You see, there's no salt content."

The High Priestess made her descent
  into the glow of the lamp.
An uncanny feeling crept over our camp
  but none of us knew why.

The mummy of Pyramidion opened one eye.
  "My beauty," he whispered to her,
  "shall never die."

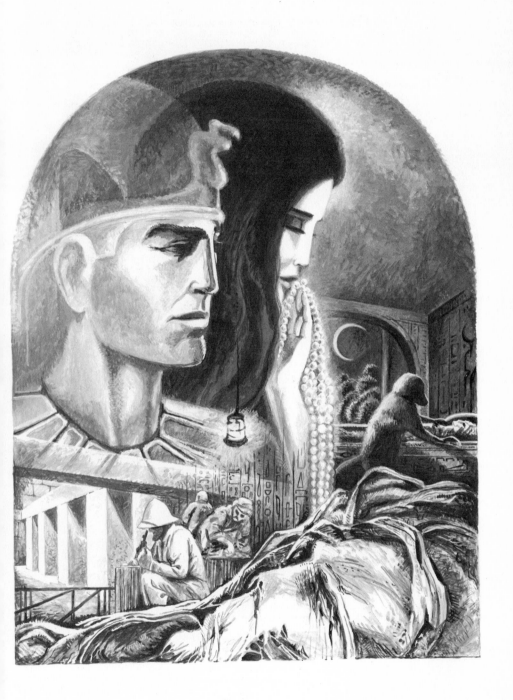

141

And now, far down the avenue,
Gustav Claudin came into view,
a scarecrow held above the horizon.
Sun behind him, shadow wizened,
he came along, swaying with fatigue,
but wondering who she'd been,
that young woman who'd appeared to him
not as some familiar intrigue of the night
but wearing a gown of light
that rippled like a wind-swept pool,
and on her brow a jewel
· that seemed to grow in size
until it filled Claudin's eyes.

  "Blanche! Blanche d'Antigny!
  Is it you that I see?"

But the young woman vanished like a mood,
and Claudin, never one to intrude,
left the moonlit mist of the lamppost unmarred
and passed by it to morning, on the boulevard.

"Many," said the skull, "have visited me."
We'd opened the tomb, cleared the debris.
Now our campfire burned and the skull was speaking,
its ancient jawbone creaking.

"Robbers took my crown and staff,
and the record of my battles.
I am left with only a laugh
and a mouth that rattles.

"But I shall tell you of my land . . ."
The dark eye sockets winked
and the time-worn tomb seemed to sink
deeper into the sand.

"Here grew the fragrant incense tree
and lions of high pedigree.
The women—let me tell you of their charms—"
The mummy raised his brittle arms
and gestured with clicking fingers.
"Their perfume lingers down through time,
and though I am turned to lime, I remember."

Within his eyes there glowed an ember.
Deep in the cavernous head
we saw the desire of the dead.

"Yes, and there was a sacred writ—
    a single page of it
    gave one power to charm a meteor, a multitude.
    Thieves burned it on this floor
    to heat their food.
I ask you, gentlemen, does not time turn all things to good use?
But these are the reflections of a skull, a recluse."

Dust spilled from the fragile mouth
and the mummy pointed to the south.
"Dried-up eyes cannot weep.
I am bones piled in a heap.
Was this a king?
I myself am forgetting . . ."

The fire danced, lighting our faces,
the professor poured from a hanging coffeepot.
The skull smiled, "This, my immortal oasis,
which even thieves have forgot."

A thin veneer of flesh crackled at his mouth
as he told us of his conquest to the south
and of his dancers with ivory wands,
    of sacred crocodile ponds
and love letters hidden in a sycamore tree.
"She was aligned to the monarchy,
and wore a double-tooth comb of bone in her hair.
That is her arm you found on the stair."

The skull fell back, neck bones snapping.
We rewound his linen wrapping
and adjusted his pillow.
"She was slender as the willow, my friends,
within her colored gown."

Gently we laid him down and closed the lid.
A wind blew round the pyramid
and a stuffed falcon gazed at us
from behind the sarcophagus,
its glass eye blinking
as if the bird were thinking
of some way it might fly again
to the kings of the delta, to the quarries,
    to the military camp.

"The batteries in this wretched lamp . . ." said the professor,
groping his way toward our tent.

At dawn we were told we must leave the monument.
"Hostilities," said the official, "have broken out at the borders.
I am sorry, but these are my orders,
    I tried to speak to the ambassadress . . ."

The professsor stood motionless. "It is as I feared."
He turned toward the king's hawk,
but the bird had disappeared.

We closed the door on the dried king,
and his whispering.
"She wore her hair in 30 strands
and played the tambourine,
a queen of slender hands
and eyes of aquamarine."

Our expedition withdrew,
down the buried avenue,
as a fighter plane streaked overhead,
and a white plume descended on the house of the dead.

The life of a god they gave him . . .
  (with) eternal breath
  Ziusudra the King . . .
  seed of humanity
in Dilmun, land of the sunrise
          (rest of the column broken away)
A mandate from the people . . .
  Senate and House support . . .
  President determined to avoid
          (next 37 lines destroyed)
devising new strategy . . .
  proliferation of nuclear weaponry
          (rest of the document destroyed)

Gustav Claudin met her again
now at a bookseller's stall.
The river, her conspirator,
laid fog upon the embankment wall
and round the seller's lair.

The mist was in the woman's hair,
her gown seemed made of it,
her form indefinite,
as women of dreams can be.

"Blanche! Blanche d'Antigny!
Is it you that I see?"
Claudin hurried toward her
but the mist was all that he met—
she had crossed the border into silhouette
leaving both the seller and Claudin
with the fading image of a fan,
feathers bound in tortoise shell
closing together in farewell.

"She was reading this book . . ."
The seller glanced at the spine,
his brow slowly knitting.
"But this is not one of mine . . ."

Around the seller's lamp a moth was flitting,
    its wings a disguise,
    a pattern of eyes that winked at Claudin through a veil.
"This book," he asked, "is it for sale?"

"Take it," said the seller, "as a gift,
for the night seems enchanted and my soul adrift."

Claudin took the book to his café
and, as night gave way to day
he turned the pages
but could not understand
this script from the ancient land of Ur.

Still, some perfume of the ages
rose up from it,
bringing images to his mind,
of form indefinite,
like sunbeams intertwined,
from which more substantial figures came,
and finally the priestess, sheathed in flame.

With incandescent wire,
fingers tipped by fire,
she shaped the circuitry of repose,
the glowing replica of a rose.
His eyelids fell,
he reached a dream hand toward her. "Mademoiselle . . ."

The owner of the café turned in surprise.
Was that Claudin, closing his eyes?
Was the great insomniac of the boulevards asleep?
He signaled the waiters to creep past Claudin's chair,
to seat the morning crowd elsewhere,
to leave a circle of silence round the tortured soul,
who'd slumped face-down in his bowl,
who'd passed at last into slumber,
for the first time in nights without number.

Gustav Claudin's dream of her was deep,
    the dream of the insomniac
    and the veiled woman of the zodiac.

158

He kneels in the dream
on the wheel of the hours
and offers to her
armfuls of flowers.